CW00816275

Other books by Martin Bailey

The Useful Book of Gadgets, Gizmos and Apps (2nd Edition)
Learn to Use a PC in 90 Minutes
Building a website using a CMS in 90 Minutes (2nd Edition)
Get more visitors to your website in 90 Minutes
Marketing your Business (2nd Edition)

ISBN 978-1-5272-4926-4

How to implement a manufacturing system

How to implement a manufacturing system

Best practices and pitfalls when implementing an MRP/ERP system

Martin Bailey

How to implement a manufacturing system

Contents

Foreword

By Dave Tudor, Editorial Director
Production Engineering Solutions magazine

The future of manufacturing is distinctly data driven.

At one end of the spectrum we're talking Smart Factories, Industry 4.0, The Internet of Things (IoT) and Big Data. Machines, equipment and processes communicate with each other, sometimes across factories in different countries and continents in real-time.

Not only that but they're intelligent; a coordinate measuring machine (CMM) hooked up to a machine tool for example, will not only highlight when a component is drifting out of tolerance; it will 'talk' directly to the machine and correct the process bringing it back into specification – seamlessly and autonomously without any human intervention.

All this is made possible through data collection - but that is only part of the story. The real key to success is doing something meaningful with it.

But for every company using data to feed and drive their Smart factories, there will be many others using it simply to improve processes and run their businesses more efficiently.

In this ultra-competitive world, investment in new technology is vital to maximise productivity – but equally as important is optimising the resources you already have.

In a production environment, this encompasses the many challenges every manufacturing company faces each and every day: things like not running out of raw materials; not having machines sitting idle; shop floor capacity planning; providing accurate quotations and estimates to customers; stock control; purchase order processing and quality control.

Get these things right and your business will thank you for it. Running a company proactively rather than reactively will make you more dynamic and able to respond to your customers' needs.

You will be able to provide much more accurate lead-times to your clients and use your available resources much more efficiently. You will know what you need and when you'll need it. You will be able to forecast better and there'll be no duplication of effort. You will sleep better at night!

However, none of this happens by accident and that's why, in my opinion, investing in high quality ERP/MRP production control software is a very good idea.

When a company has money to invest, it's very tempting to rush out and buy the latest all-singing, all-dancing machine tool. I certainly wouldn't underestimate the importance of keeping up with the latest technology, but it's not the full story.

For a comparatively modest outlay, you could invest in software that will underpin the entire business, linking the constituent parts together harmoniously and efficiently, making you more productive and ultimately profitable.

There are several excellent ERP/MRP/production software packages available in the marketplace and I have written about most of them in my role as Editor of Production Engineering Solutions. However, one that particularly impressed me was 123insight.

Like similar packages in the marketplace, the software is intuitive, simple to learn and use and cost-effective, but what's different about 123insight is its business model. The first point to note is that there's no salesman – 123 Insight gets the word out by inviting companies to attend free Evaluation Workshops which are held regularly at venues up and down the country.

This is a risk-free process: the 2 ½ hour workshops are all about educating and informing rather than selling. I attended a workshop in 2017 and was impressed not only by the user-friendliness and power of the software, but also the professionalism of the 123 Insight staff and relaxed atmosphere.

But whatever product you choose, there's no doubt that the management of good quality data is the cornerstone of any successful business and software is the glue that holds everything together.

It's a sound investment.

Dave Tudor
Editorial Director
Production Engineering Solutions
www.pesmedia.com

About Martin Bailey and 123 Insight Ltd

123 Insight Ltd was formed in 2000. Originally under the name Rent-IT Systems, it was the first MRP system to be available on a subscription-only basis, which in turn became a trailblazer in driving the software market in this direction. Having either been nominated for or won over three dozen awards since 2007, the system itself is provided on a risk-free basis. Prospective companies can see the software at Evaluation Workshops held around the UK each month. If they like what they see they can register to attend the 'No Obligation' training on the understanding that if they decide not to proceed with 123insight they can walk away with nothing to pay thereafter (and with a lot more knowledge than when they started). After that, they can register to receive the software and have all the knowledge they need to implement it themselves but with the backup and support of 123 Insight Ltd behind them. The 123 Insight training and implementation team are on-hand to lead them through the implementation process, and the Help Desk is there to provide telephone and remote desktop support. On average, 123insight customers call the Help Desk once per month.

I have been the Marketing Manager of 123 Insight Ltd since 2002 and have written dozens of case studies on existing users across all types of manufacturing types and sizes. This has allowed me to identify the problems associated with not having a manufacturing system or having an ineffective solution – whether it be home-grown or a packaged system.

This book was a natural progression from the case studies, which were designed to help 123insight prospective customers see the real-world and knock-on benefits of a well-implemented MRP system. While the case studies would give them comfort that

companies of similar size or industry type had benefited from such a system, they were often still fearful of making the leap themselves. By providing a proven template of the implementation process, interwoven with anecdotal evidence of success, I hope that this will help motivate you into moving forward.

Technology has always been a passion for me – at the tender age of eleven I sold my Scalextric set to buy a Sinclair ZX81 and never looked back. This is my ninth book, with all of them covering technology or marketing in some shape or other. I've been told that I have the knack of distilling complex subjects down into something much more understandable, so hopefully this won't be too heavy or a dry read for you.

Although I'm a sucker for a shiny new gadget as much as the next geek, it's the software behind the hardware that often adds that shine and therefore it's the software that holds a greater appeal for me. Take a look at what the phone in your pocket does today versus a decade ago – while the hardware has of course improved, today's user interfaces and apps have progressed to the extent that many more people – whether young, old, with limited I.T. skills or with accessibility issues – can take advantage of them. Most people have a smart phone and therefore are much more comfortable with touch-screen technologies, which are now making in-roads into today's shop floor environments.

I hope that this book helps you to confirm that MRP is something that your manufacturing business can benefit from and gives you the confidence that it is a project that you can take on.

How to implement a manufacturing system

Introduction

When a manufacturing business is created it's an exciting time. Prototyping, working out the best manufacturing methods and then ramping up to full production. *"Let's just get the product out there – we'll worry about everything else later"* are the words often muttered.

Further down the line things start to reach breaking point. A lack of discipline in the stock room makes it difficult to find anything as people simply take what they need whenever they need it. No visibility means that you cannot plan effectively, and these issues have a combined effect of lengthening lead-times. There can also be an impact on finances, as more cash is tied up in the wrong stock, hence business can subsequently be lost due to many of the reasons mentioned above.

Inevitably, systems are created to deal with these problems – spreadsheets, a database or perhaps an in-house bespoke system. Each have their benefits in the short-term, but they have a limited shelf-life as your company expands (more on this later) but they often end up fragmented, short-sighted and perhaps unsupported. At this point your business has grown and is in even more need of a reliable data infrastructure.

It may be that you already took the plunge with MRP but things didn't go as planned. Not all MRPs are equal, and many have 'grown' into the role of MRP, often through acquiring modules developed by other companies and 'shoe-horned' into the core product, leading to a disjointed and bug-ridden result. The problem is that at this point you will have often spent tens or even hundreds of thousands of pounds. Do you risk doing that all over again? Albert Einstein has been famously incorrectly attributed as saying *"The definition of insanity is doing the same thing over and over and expecting different results"*. Don't assume this is also correct when taking a second bite out of the MRP battle. Hindsight is a wonderful thing and if you know what didn't work, you are unlikely to make the same mistake second time around.

Firstly, what is MRP?

Materials Requirement Planning is a production planning, scheduling, and inventory control system used to manage manufacturing processes. In addition to being a database to store information such as customers, products, bills of materials (BOMs), sales orders, purchase orders, works orders, etc., it also takes the legwork out of many connecting processes.

The 'MRP' process itself can be run hourly, daily or less frequently depending on the capability of the system in use. On older systems this can be a very time-consuming process. It examines the demand (e.g. what orders you've received), looks at your stock and then makes suggestions as to what you need to buy in order to fulfil the demand. It can then recommend who you should buy from and, if you agree with its suggestions, automatically raise and email the purchase orders. Moving onto production, an MRP system will allow you to create a digital workflow, based on all of your manufacturing equipment and processes, so that when you raise a works order the routes for that order are clearly defined.

A walkthrough

So, taking it from the top, MRP starts with the sales or forecasting process. All of your customers, products and prices are stored within the system. You'll be able to build quotes, create price lists and when you win business, quickly convert the quote to a sales order and provide accurate lead times.

When the MRP process is run it compares your demands (order book and/or forecasts) to your current stock and suggests replenishment Works Orders for the appropriate dates and quantities to cover any shortfalls. It can then check that you have enough components to build these Works Orders and suggests purchase orders to cover shortfalls. In doing this, it takes account of current stock, outstanding orders, minimum purchase quantity rules, etc.

Purchase orders can be placed automatically, and the system will allow both your purchasing, goods in and stores staff to keep an eye on inbound orders. The Stores Manager can quickly perform tasks such as booking stock in/out and performing stock takes.

Moving onto the shop floor, the works order follows the production process of the ordered item, with staff updating the system after each operation or stage is completed. Meanwhile, sales staff can quickly see where a job is if a customer calls for an update.

As goods filter through to despatch, staff can consolidate deliveries together as they have visibility down the line. This saves time, with courier savings also passed onto the customer.

This is a very simplistic walkthrough and doesn't consider the various real-world scenarios that your business has to cope with on a daily basis. Audits, returns, quarantining items, subcontracting and import/export are just some of the other scenarios that you'll probably have to deal with.

A good MRP system provides a common interface for all staff and handles difficult to track processes. Whether you only sell to a domestic market or worldwide, make to order or mass produce, MRP will be provide the backbone of your business, giving it room to grow and providing visibility and traceability to today's exacting quality standards.

OK, full disclosure here: As the Marketing Manager for MRP/ERP system developers 123 Insight Ltd, my aim for this book is to hope that you will consider our product. However, whatever you decide, this book will act as a useful guide and template for a successful implementation. It's packed full of real-world advice based on hundreds of customers that have implemented the system themselves. Yes, it is biased towards our methodology of implementation, and yes, it is littered with examples of 123insight customers that have benefited from installing our system. *The reason is that it simply works.* Our entire business model is based on customers being self-supporting, yet with support there when they need it – 'Lifetime care, with a light touch.'

A successful implementation hinges on commitment from the top down with managers across all departments working together. This book aims to remove the fear traditionally associated with selecting and installing MRP, demystifying many of the myths that MRP must be expensive, can only be implemented by consultants and should require additional resources to run and maintain.

123insight was designed from the ground up to be user-installable, with every single customer using the same 'off-the-shelf' product. Our philosophy of *'if it doesn't work for you, then it doesn't work for us'* means that we quickly identify and tell you if we discover that you need a feature that is outside of our scope, as there's no point in wasting your time or ours – it simply wasn't meant to be. Our business model is a low monthly subscription but with no minimum contract period. There's no colossal up-front cost, and even training is provided under no-obligation. It also gets around the issue of *'I already spent my money on an MRP system that didn't work, and now I can't afford to do it again'*.

Throughout this book you will find real-world examples, such as the one below, of the typical problems that companies faced with either in-house system or traditional systems, and how they resolved them with 123insight.

A customer serving the electronics sector had originally considered and discounted 123insight, only to spend £80k on an alternative. Six months later the system still wasn't operational – the MD chalked it up to experience, contacted us and was only able to select and implement 123insight because of the no-risk approach.

What kind of business are you?

Before you can decide what type of system you require, you need to define your business. There are generally four types of manufacturing company and although many of the needs are similar, there will be different considerations (specific to your MRP requirements) depending on which camp you fall into:

Make to order: This type of company produces low volumes of a range of products, often for other companies, with a high variation in the production cycle. Staff could be making different products every day resulting in more margin for error and less opportunity to improve manufacturing techniques. As the manufacturer often will not 'own' the product, this means that they are constrained as to how the product is manufactured and therefore cannot make design changes without consulting the client.

Quoting can often be an issue, given the wide variation, and converting quotes to sales, works and purchase orders can also be time-consuming. Also, if the demand changes it can be extremely difficult to see the impact on stock, purchasing and production.

Subcontractor (Job Shop): Similar to 'make to order' (and suffering from similar problems), subcontractors specialise in small quantities of tailor-made or custom-built parts, where each job is finished before the next one is started. Orders are less likely to be repeated and your company is not in control of the design of the product. Subcontractors often find it difficult to schedule production due to the wide range of products and differing production flow. Production runs tend to be smaller, as the design can often change which in turn limits your ability to stock large amounts.

Volume production (often making for stock): This often describes a company that is manufacturing its own product range using tried and tested methods and therefore with a lower risk of mistakes. The range of products is likely to be smaller, but the quantities for each are much larger, and often repeated. Traceability is often key, with the likes of food manufacturers needing to be able to track either from ingredient to products or vice versa.

Electronics manufacturers will often need to track serial numbers of components as well as the finished product. For companies adhering to quality standards such as ISO9001:2015, tracking of staff skills in relation to manufacturing will also be a consideration.

Bespoke Project Manufacturer: These companies are invariably making one-off or very low quantities of products that are unlikely to be repeated, often with massive bills of materials running into the thousand or even tens of thousands. As with the Make to Stock producer, traceability of serialised components is often key. Such projects also often have a service element to them and may need to track initial product performance prior to shipping as well as the unit being returned for service or repair in the future.

Now that we have broadly defined our manufacturing types and some of their common problems, it should be clear that although there is greater importance on some issues (such as serial tracking) for some company types, all manufacturers essentially need the same thing – a framework with which to build their business on.

Regardless of what your company makes, your basic needs will be the same – the ability to control and track the flow of information in every step from initial enquiry all the way through to finished product.

How to implement a manufacturing system

MRP versus ERP

Many companies mistakenly believe (or are steered into the decision by consultants with a vested interest) that they need ERP over an MRP system. But what is the difference and where do you draw the line between those that need it and those that don't?

ERP stands for Enterprise Resource Planning and is defined as 'an information system designed to coordinate the resources, information and processes within an organisation'. It comprises of a common database that provides interfaces and information to every department within the business.

Depending on which definition of MRP you follow there are different interpretations – Materials Requirement Planning (MRP) and Manufacturing Resource Planning (MRP II), which then evolved into ERP. As ERP systems have developed, some have moved away from their manufacturing roots. This has resulted in failed implementations due to the chosen ERP system's processes no longer matching the business requirements.

ERP covers areas such as:

- Accounting (nominal, sales and purchase ledgers, fixed assets, etc)
- Human resources (payroll, time sheets, training etc)

- Manufacturing (bill of materials, quality control (QC), managing the manufacturing process, etc.)
- Supply chain (stock control, purchasing, scheduling)
- CRM (sales and marketing, support and customer service)
- Project management (managing costs, time and activities)
- Data warehousing (document management)

Many of these areas are already covered either partially or completely by MRP. The perceived benefit of ERP is to have a single solution to manage an entire company's information structure and processes, only requiring a single vendor and potentially ironing out data conflicts between different applications.

Where does MRP stop and ERP start?

MRP systems focus on the processes from sales forecasting through to invoicing but traditionally tend to exclude processes such as CRM and accounting.

Some systems have evolved through acquisition of companies that produce one element (such as CRM) and trying to integrate it to the core product, rebranding it in the process to disguise its origins. More often than not, the end result is a mixture of two or more systems which may not be very stable, have a different user interface to the rest of the system and does not provide the completely seamless solution they aspire to.

Issues with ERP over MRP implementation

Due to its breadth of coverage across an organisation the problems associated with implementing ERP over MRP will be greater by default, potentially increasing risk of failure. More departments are affected, and legacy data for each area of the business needs to be manipulated into a format where it can be migrated. The setup of the system is also important – many make the mistake of mirroring the setup of their legacy systems, thus carrying on the mistakes of yesteryear.

While many implementers successfully switch over to a new single system, for others this can prove too much to achieve in one hit. A more flexible approach is to allow companies to implement at their own pace, rolling the system out to specific departments first rather than forcing the entire company to go live from day one.

'Best in class' is the best

The best practice should be to select the 'best in class' product for the task at hand. If, for example an ERP's built-in accounts facility is lacking or less suited to your business, then a better solution is a separate MRP and account system that can communicate with each other. Maybe you already have a tried and trusted accounts system and are considering your first foray into manufacturing software. Simple – keep the accounts software that you know and love and get a manufacturing system that works for you and links to your accounts software.

The cost of ERP over MRP also plays an important factor – in a game of Scrabble the letter E may have the lesser value than M, but the choice of the letter at the front of your chosen system can have a major impact on your balance sheet without proportional improvements to your business.

Where does 123insight fit into this?

123insight positions itself as a Manufacturing Enterprise Management system. It focuses on the core competence of manufacturing and is suitable for all types, shapes and sizes of companies up to enterprise-level. (Our smallest customer has just two staff with the largest having over 4500). The core system is referred to as MRP, but as there are options for CRM and integration to accounts systems this bridges the gap between MRP and ERP. The Software Development Kit (SDK) provides a safe and secure method of passing data into

123insight from 3rd party systems (such as machine monitoring, electronic scales, intranets, websites, CAD, etc.)

The bottom line is that you shouldn't rule out MRP because you have been told to look at ERP. Also, don't think that by selecting MRP today you are painting yourself into a corner further down the road. The right system will be able to grow with your business.

Now that we have established the basics, let's focus on what is likely to be your current reality. I make no apologies if the next chapter triggers deep-seated emotions or induces hyperventilation, as we need to confront these issues to understand how MRP can overcome them!

> *A company manufacturing components for the motorsports industry replaced their 20+ year old DOS-based production system with 123insight. They restructured their works orders to also include instructions for staff, renaming them to 'assembly instruction sheets', making it much easier for new staff to understand manufacturing processes.*

How to implement a manufacturing system

Before MRP – your current problems

As already discussed, you are most likely reading this from the point of three current scenarios – you're using a collection of Excel spreadsheets and/or paper-based systems, you have created and subsequently outgrown a bespoke system, or have already invested in a 'packaged' system which is no longer fit for purpose.

There are initial benefits and drawbacks from starting with each system:

Excel Spreadsheets/Paper-based

This is invariably how every small company starts, before looking at MRP, even if it's just to prove out systems and workflows or to start collating and shaping data with a view to moving to another system. Most people have some understanding of Excel, so it's very quick to just knock out a spreadsheet in a format that staff will be able to understand and manipulate.

The first problem is that only one person can work on a spreadsheet at any given time. If you have the stock list spreadsheet open and someone else wants to add or amend to it, they'll either potentially be reading out of date data or not be able to open it at all (due to file locking). Many companies print and distribute such documents, often daily, which means that you have no guarantee that what you are looking at is correct within minutes of printing it.

Multiply this by the number of departments in your business that are creating similar spreadsheets and you end up with complete fragmentation, making traceability and forward-planning somewhere between difficult and impossible.

Imagine trying to perform an audit for a quality assessor where you need to prove when something was made, how, by whom and with what components – all of these will most probably be scattered across your company, perhaps residing on individual hard drives, or at the very least buried across folders on your server.

> *Prior to installing 123insight, one customer had to prove a patent infringement by demonstrating that they had purchased a specific component type before a competing company. It was only after days of frantic searching that they came across an old invoice by chance – something that they could have retrieved in seconds with 123insight using the drill-down capability.*

We've established that electronic documents have their issues but move onto paper-based systems and the problem gets even worse. Aside from the obvious issues, such as paperwork getting lost, many lose sight of the fact that it takes a lot of manpower to 'push' paperwork around a factory. Like spreadsheets, paper is only as up to date as the electronic file that it was produced from, so keeping documents in sync requires further resources.

Documents such as Works Orders often exist in multi-part format, with one copy destined for admin and the other for accounts. Obviously, this has an environmental impact and can often add a considerable cost over time.

> One 123insight user managed to remove several printers from their offices and factory because of the reduction in paper usage, while another moved from expensive bespoke pre-printed paper to 123insight's customisable documents.
>
> Many customers cite a 50% or greater reduction of paper after going live, as all staff can view documents such as quotes or works, sales and purchase orders online. Furthermore, any other document type can be automatically attached to these items, so you could send a product brochure PDF out with a quote, or a Certificate of Conformity (CoC) with a despatch note.

Bespoke System

Companies often go the bespoke route because they have already experienced the pain of 'Excel Hell' and a member of staff has the capability to write something themselves. This will generally be based around an Access database or similar and will be highly customised to meet their needs.

One thing that we hear on almost every training session is *'Ahh, but our company is very different'*. Normally, by the end of the day they realise that they are actually no different to any other manufacturer – raw materials go in, processes happen to them and then the finished product emerges. It's that simple. There may be variances, such as additional processes happening via subcontract services.

Bespoke systems on the surface appear to offer the best solution – they are tailor-made to match every aspect of the company, its products and their methods of manufacture, but for many it's a case of reinventing the wheel but coming up with a square.

Any production management system is performing very complex tasks under the surface. As your business and its product range/methods of manufacture grow, the system needs to be able to expand to cope. That's fine if you have a team of competent programmers that can dedicate the time to code, test and roll out new features in a controlled manner. In the real world, of course, this is not how it happens. It'll often be one person within the company that already has a role (often quite senior), that has enough experience to develop something usable. It might cover stock control, quoting or basic production management, but rarely does it cover the realms of true MRP. Maybe it was designed in the days when your company focussed on small runs, but now you're into mass production with a wide range of components and complex bills of materials. Purchasing becomes a nightmare and processes that were fine when there was only a small order to deal with gradually become extremely time-consuming.

> *The MD of an electronics company had developed an Access database to handle purchasing. After rapid expansion, the company won an order which subsequently took two weeks to raise all the purchase orders for using the bespoke system. 'I'm never, ever doing that again' were his comments, as he started to research MRP, found 123insight and was live just seven weeks later.*

Then, one day, the developer decides to leave. The minute the ink is dry on their P45 your company is on borrowed time. Any required changes either require expensive subcontracting or simply get left, and god forbid the system falls over, perhaps because of a Windows update or other problem elsewhere. New systems (often our 'old friends' Excel and paper) spring up to compensate for the inadequacies of the bespoke system, and as data continues to grow across each system the problem just multiples.

Packaged System

A packaged system is essentially an off-the-shelf product that should meet most of your needs. The traditional approach has always been that the software is 'purchased' up-front (even though you never really own it) for a five or six-figure sum, spend a similar amount in consultancy to bend it to meet your needs and then spend around 15-20% of that software cost every year for maintenance/support. Companies often then find they must fork out for every additional customisation or report, plus whenever a major new version appears there will be an upgrade fee plus engineer time associated with installing it.

A common issue can best be described as 'the tail wagging the dog'. Companies have implemented a system and found that they have to modify their processes, often to detrimental effect, in order to accommodate the system rather than the other way around. A good system will be designed to meet the needs of its users with minimal or no customisation.

There is a sub-category of the packaged system: industry-specific systems. You may have considered evaluating software designed specifically for your industry, but just because it says that it's been designed with 'you' in mind there is no guarantee that it will meet your needs. Often, such systems have been developed by a company in your industry for internal use and someone then had the bright idea to market the product. In effect, these are bespoke products that try to claim that because they are specific to your industry, they are better than generic solutions. However, generally they were designed to meet the perceived needs of just one company. You'll often find that rather than the product meeting more of your needs than a more general system it actually contains functionality so niche that renders it near unusable.

A biscuit manufacturer initially relied on a series of Excel spreadsheets and decided to evaluate bakery-specific production software. After investigating the market, they found that solutions were not flexible enough for their needs. They subsequently implemented 123insight thereby reducing their lead times and stock levels in the process.

Another regular problem is the 'rusted handcuffs' problem. Companies implement a system only to find that the product is discontinued a few years down the line or, worse still, the vendor has gone out of business altogether. You are tied to the system with no prospect to upgrade and potentially no support for any problems. If there is a new version – perhaps based on an entirely new platform – the cost often compares to buying an entirely new system, and of course you can expect to pay huge consultancy fees to migrate your system over.

There are many well-publicised horror stories of MRP/ERP implementation failures, few more prominent than Montclair State University and Oracle. Montclair claimed that they originally contracted Oracle for a system worth $4.3m, but due to serious mistakes and delays by Oracle it would now cost up to $20m more. They accused Oracle of missing deadlines, using unprepared staff and even rigging demos to suggest features were included in the core system. Oracle subsequently counter-sued, claiming that Montclair's actions were to cover their own shortcomings. They settled out of court after two years of legal wrangling.

> *An electronics company had been working with a DOS-based MRP system since the 1990's. They upgraded to the latest Windows version in the mid-2000's (at considerable cost) only to be told a few months later that the product would be discontinued. They were only able to select 123insight due to its subscription model, having already spent a large amount on the previous system's update, and were live in just 7 weeks.*

In fact, a study showcased in Computer Weekly magazine, published in February 2018, also stated that businesses have less than a 50% chance of an SAP software implementation succeeding. The survey of 113 individuals across 105 companies for the *'Uncovering the factors that drive success for SAP customers study'* from SAP advisory service Resulting IT, found that only 36% felt their SAP project kept to its original plan and just under half (48%) said their project failed to achieve business objectives.

123insight falls into the 'packaged system' category but differentiates itself through its flexibility, low vendor dependency, low monthly subscription, no-risk approach to implementation and no hidden extras. Every single customer is using the same system without any core customisation due to its versatility.

If you're reading this and recognising some of the highlighted issues within your own company, then you're ready to move on. However, just because *you* are ready it doesn't mean that everyone within your business is on board. So, before you start considering new systems you need to make sure that everyone is in agreement.

How to implement a manufacturing system

MRP and finance (accounts software)

This chapter is more of a sideways step for many companies, as you may have an accounts system that you have no plans to change, and also may not be planning on much, if any integration between accounts and manufacturing.

Most, if not all of your company's departments will be involved with the selection of a new manufacturing system, but the same tends not to be true of an accounts system.

Accounts software tends to be one of the first systems set up in any company, but manufacturing software often comes much later. If you currently do not have an MRP system you will already have identified with many of the issues mentioned earlier – especially duplication of data. So, when selecting a manufacturing system, it's important to consider how the two will communicate and what level of integration is required.

Some manufacturing systems will also have an accounts offering and companies will often move away from their previous accounting software in order to implement a combined manufacturing/accounts solution, but this not always the best solution.

One such example was an existing 123insight user was told by a consultant that they should consider an ERP system with fully integrated accounts. They had been using 123insight for nearly five years but were told that moving to an integrated solution would 'take them to the next level'. One year on, a lot of heartache and over £100,000 later and the system still wasn't working correctly. The final nail in the coffin was a stock take that resulted in duplicated serial numbers. They returned immediately to 123insight adding an interface to Sage 50 accounts which subsequently met all of their needs. It's worth noting that they were only able to return to 123insight because of the low monthly subscription – if they had had to choose another system they would have had to spend a similar amount, with no guarantee of success.

What does 'integrated accounts' even mean?

Usually, a vendor that has an MRP/ERP system where accounts is provided as part of the product brand will refer to it as 'integrated'. It may be that started out as one product (e.g. accounts) and grew over time, often through acquisition, to include the other (e.g. MRP). When a vendor buys a software company in order to integrate the product into their own it tends to be a mixed bag. As a standalone product it may well have been strong, but there are many horror stories of disjointed interfaces and functionality that does not cross over between key areas of the software.

However, integration does not have to be between two products from the same supplier. Many systems – both MRP and accounts – are designed to allow simple and easy data exchange. In fact, any system that did not offer such facilities would be 'dead in the water'. Customers expect systems to be able to play nicely with each other and it's often seen as a commercial consideration that only benefits the vendor when connectivity and functionality that should be simple is blocked. Apple's 'walled garden' is a prime example, with many apps unable to offer the same functionality available in their Android equivalent because of restrictions that Apple places on the operating system.

What 'integration' do I really need?

This is the real 'nuts and bolts' of it. Your sales and purchasing departments would generally need to know information such as credit limits, accounts on stop, outstanding invoices and payments made for both customers and suppliers. Staff may need to be able to quickly make decisions such as 'can I take this order?' or 'am I able to order these parts?'. It may also be important for your despatch department to have visibility of a customer's status as the situation may have changed since the order was placed.

123insight's accounts connectivity options provides tight integration with popular accounts systems such as Sage 50/Sage 200, Access Dimensions and Xero and allows sophisticated rules to be created, providing warnings or aborting transactions based on credit status. This ensures that you can choose the best accounts system for your company's needs without compromising on your manufacturing system.

Do I really need that level of integration?

Smaller companies often feel that the fully integrated solution is a sledgehammer to crack a nut. Perhaps they have several licences of accounts software or their business is structured in such a way that financial controls are not necessary within the MRP software itself. Your only consideration then is ensuring that information is in sync between the two systems – namely the sales and purchase ledgers. This in itself should not be a major undertaking – after all, the data you are passing from one system to another should be similar.

However, there are certain considerations. There may (read: should) be levels of security to protect data from possible corruption during import from MRP to accounts, so you need to ensure that any data is validated and logged during import.

So, how do you choose a new accounts system?

All of these points go to reinforce the mantra mentioned earlier that 'best in class is the best'. Different accounting packages have different strengths. Depending on your business, some will be more suitable than others. For example, for companies using multi-currency and operating in different countries the selected system must be able to support different taxation laws.

While your manufacturing software provides a backbone for your business it's the financial software that controls the lifeblood. How you choose your manufacturing and accounting systems will depend on which direction you are coming from. Maybe you are happy with your accounting system and looking to implement MRP for the first time but are wondering if you need something all-encompassing. Or perhaps you've outgrown your existing accounts software and are not sure whether replacing like-for-like is going to stunt growth further down the line. From the 123insight perspective all of the bases are covered. There are a range of connectivity options, from simple data exchange through to tight integration with all major accounting systems. All that remains is to select the right accounting tool for the job and choose the level of connectivity required.

How to implement a manufacturing system

Winning hearts and minds

Before you move head-long into selection and subsequent implementation, it's important to accept that not everyone in your organisation will be as enthusiastic as you are about the possibility of installing a company-wide system such as MRP. So, it's therefore equally important that you look at this through the eyes of others and handle each person's concerns sensitively.

There are a variety of issues at play here, and you can categorise individuals as having one or more of the following traits:

The protectionist

This person is king or queen of their domain. They take tasks on board rather than telling you how to do them, for fear of making their position weaker, often resulting in an overload of work. Information is stored in their heads and taking time off often results in urgent calls to interrupt their holiday. They'll often have created home-grown systems that are indecipherable to others to handle tasks, relying on them to maintain and expand them. They'll see an MRP system as a threat to their position, but it needn't be so. Include them in the early stages, making them a 'champion' for their department. They'll quickly see the benefits, but by being integral to the implementation this will sate any concerns they have about obsolescence.

A good MRP system will have a common interface across all areas, so raising a purchase order should be no different to a sales order or quote. This ensures that staff aren't helpless in their absence and can often cover for other departments during times of holiday or sickness.

The technophobe

This person never really wanted to escalate above the ability to master light switches and struggles with even the most basic task of locating a file on your network or editing an Excel spreadsheet. Indeed, my own mother broke down in tears when (in the late 80's) she was presented firstly with an electronic typewriter followed in short succession with a PC. Often, they'll be in roles that require little interaction with technology, such as on the shop floor. The advent of shop floor terminals that they'll have to interactive with will fill them with dread. However, these same people will invariably have tablets and smartphones at home and are more technically literate than they themselves believe. If their access requirements are limited, ensure that you only train them on what they need to know. Give them access to other users that can give assistance when required.

In addition to user training, 123 Insight provides all training documentation in electronic format, allowing them to be customised for downstream training. This makes it easy to give specific staff only the help they need without information overkill.

The paranoid

There are those that will see MRP as big brother, especially if you are implementing shop floor data control to record job timings. Every form of monitoring will be seen as a stick to beat them with so it's important to highlight 'the carrot'.

> *A manufacturer in the food sector implemented 123insight using its skills matrix initially as part of their quality accreditation but then extended it to be a part of their profit share scheme. Staff that initially saw the system as a drawback felt the benefit in their pay packet as their performance and ability to take on more complex tasks delivered bonuses.*

The traditionalist

Everyone has reservations about change, but there are those that find even the smallest tweak to their daily routines too much to bear. To counteract this, examine their existing role and identify where they are most likely to see the benefits. Ensure that they understand exactly what the system means for their role – don't just expect them to understand the implementations for them from being told about 'the bigger picture'.

> *A medical instrument manufacturer implemented 123insight, but initially encountered resistance from the Stores Manager. After using the system for a few months, they agreed to a case study, with the same manager happily admitting that after his initial scepticism he is now the system's firmest advocate.*

As you can see, there's a pattern here – these are all about emotions and insecurities. We all have them. By being sensitive to possible concerns you can be proactive about dealing with many issues before they even arise.

There is one more important character type to try to identify within a business – The Gatekeeper. This person may or may not exhibit some of the above personality traits, but they will be someone that holds significant influence with those around them, whether this is at management or shop floor level. Get this person on-side and they'll become your ally in tackling all of the personnel-related issues that this project is likely to encounter.

Planning your selection process

You are now at the point whereby you've accepted that you need an MRP system to take your company to the next level (or, more likely, to take control of the problems your current system is causing), and enough senior management are in agreement. What next?

Firstly, understand that a manufacturing system implementation is a business-led project, not an IT one. Software is only a quarter of what's important. We'll cover this more in the next chapter.

Before you can consider starting the selection process you need to define your company's needs. What functions are essential, what are nice to have and what are surplus to requirements?

Deciding on your show-stoppers

Your 'show-stoppers' are the functions that your company cannot do without, and these should be the questions at the top of your list. There's no point looking at ancillary functionality if the core requirements are not met. Remember, think about your requirements down the road, not just today. For example, maybe you're thinking of an ISO accreditation, expanding into different product ranges or breaking into new markets. Each of these may require functions that you won't necessarily take advantage of today but will certainly need in the future.

Ironically, many of the questions posed against an MRP system don't relate to the function of MRP itself. Each department will have its own requirements. One approach is to follow a selection of orders from quotation to despatch, making a note of any unique requirements.

Let's take a quick look at some of the common ones:

Sales Department

The ability to create a sales order is a given but are you also able to build a quote, and then quickly convert that to an order? Can you create price lists? What about despatching to a different location to the invoice? Can product brochure PDFs be automatically attached and sent alongside a quote?

Finance/Accounting

As covered earlier, some manufacturing systems will have their own integrated accounts (which means that you have to dump your current system), but the best of breed approach is to ensure that you have the most suitable manufacturing and accounts systems playing nicely together. If your business sells internationally, then your MRP needs multi-currency support. It also needs to match Purchase Orders, Sales Orders, support nominal codes, allow for sales credits/purchase debits and provide advance sales invoices.

Purchasing

This is one of the departments often most (positively) affected by MRP, so it's important to cover all your bases here. In addition to being able to raise a purchase order manually, check if the system can automatically place orders that it recommends when the MRP process is run.

For MRP to offer realistic purchasing suggestions you'll need to be able to store price lists from multiple suppliers, taking into account quantity price breaks. If you have an internal approval process on orders and requisitions, will the system respect this? Will the system allow you to raise and track quotes? Finally, what about items that fall out of the category of 'stock items', such as services?

Stores

If purchasing can be positively affected by MRP then the stores department is where you're likely to see the most drastic savings with the right system. The parts you stock will determine your key questions. Do you have items with a shelf-life that need to be tracked, such as paints or resins? Do you need to operate a 'first in, first out' (FIFO) policy? With mobile devices becoming more prevalent, will your chosen system offer staff the ability to check or transfer stock on a tablet rather than being chained to a desk?

Planning

Capacity is not a simple spreadsheet of hours in the week – many factors come into play. A good MRP system will let you create each resource, allowing you to plan for your available capacity. Furthermore, you should be able to see the effect of accepting suggestions made by MRP on your capacity before accepting them.

Production

As said before, although every company thinks that their production processes are unique, manufacturing generally boils down to taking raw components and applying a process – be it manufacturing or assembly. A good MRP system needs to allow you to define and track each of these processes, including functions such as subcontracting, alternative routings (e.g. the ability to manufacture a product a different way, etc.). If you use serialised components, such as in the electronics industry, how detailed does your serial tracking need to be – just the serial of the final shipped unit, or do you need to track multiple components within the finished product? You also need to be able to log progress for each operation and be able to attribute time to operators, so the ability to quickly log this on the shop floor is a must.

Goods In/Despatch

Managing the flow of items in and out of your facility is extremely important in ensuring that lead times are met. You will need to have visibility of what's due in and, more importantly, what's due to be shipped out. If you ship goods to the same customer regularly, perhaps even several shipments a day, then the ability to see what's coming down the line and even combine deliveries not only saves on courier costs, but it saves time and packing resources. Other facilities such as being able to factor in landed costs for imported goods can also be important.

Although creating your selection criteria is important, ensure that you are open to the possibility that there may be a better way than your current methods. Just because you've been doing things a certain way, it doesn't mean there isn't a more efficient alternative out there. More importantly, by hanging onto 'tried and trusted' methods you might be painting yourself into a corner in the future. Having said that, be aware that some vendors might be trying to persuade you to make a significant change to your methods simply because they cannot deliver the capability that you need.

How to implement a manufacturing system

Planning – What NOT to do

Time and time again there are some common errors made at the start of the selection process, so in this chapter we're going to explore them and demonstrate how you can avoid these pitfalls.

It's a Business System, not an I.T. System

"It's software, so it's an I.T. project, right?" Wrong! Your I.T. department will of course have the skillsets to handle the hardware and software implications of the project but may have no idea of the needs of each individual department.

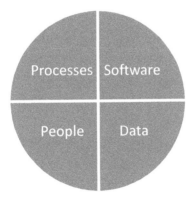

The project encompasses four main areas:

- **Software**, along with associated hardware requirements

- **Data** – exporting, cleansing, re-shaping and importing. Also, understanding your data's current structure and reviewing whether this can benefit from change going forward
- **People** – training, managing expectation and ensuring commitment. It is people that drive the project forward and that will either make it a success or failure
- **Processes** – what you do today versus what you need to do going forward. Do you need to re-examine your current processes to see whether they are still fit for purpose as you move forward?

Team effort, not a one-man project

In all but the smallest of companies you will need to create a team of key individuals from your business. Expecting one person to understand the demands of each department is unrealistic, and invariably there will also be inter-departmental politics to deal with. By having key players from all main departments, you ensure that the needs for each area of the business can be addressed. You'll also embed a 'level of redundancy', so that knowledge is not confined to only one individual. Many companies are in the position of needing to change system because of this very problem.

Top-level commitment

A project of this magnitude needs commitment from the top of the tree. Management cannot expect to say to staff 'make it happen' and then hand off the project, paying little attention during the selection and (if you get that far) implementation process. Senior management need to fully understand what any proposed system is aiming to do and be involved at every major step to ensure that your goals are met.

Unrealistic estimation of time

It is vital that project leaders appreciate that such a project will take resources away from your business. Staff will need training and time will be taken to handle data migration, structuring of the new system, downstream training, testing, etc. Allocating too little or too long a time can each have a detrimental impact on your ability to get the project over the line. Too little, and staff are overwhelmed and unable to meet deadlines – too long and the project simply fizzles out through lack of focus.

Don't force a square peg into a round hole

We touched on this in the previous chapter, but it's important to hammer this point home. It's very easy to be seduced by salespeople saying *'yes, we can customise our system to fit your way of working'*, but have you considered that your current processes may not actually be the most efficient? Remember also that customisation of a system moves it away from being 'standard', making future software upgrades more problematic and, inevitably, more costly.

Just because you've always done something one way it does not follow that it's the most efficient. One manufacturing company used a 'raffle ticket' system, whereby key departments would have different colour raffle tickets. As a works order passed through each department staff would attach a different colour of the same raffle ticket number onto it. Once it reached the end of its journey and all of the 'colours' were attached it was deemed 'OK to invoice'. This system was of course fraught with inefficiencies, but it was the only system that staff knew. When they came to look for a new system they started by asking 'can it do this?'. Therefore, be open to the prospect of considering alternative processes. They may work for you or they may not, but if you approach it with an open mind you may be pleasantly surprised by the new possibilities that present themselves.

Don't set false barriers on implementation timing

Many companies delay implementing MRP under the misapprehension that it will be better to do it after a certain deadline has passed – often the end of the financial year. There may be a valid reason for delaying, such as a factory move but waiting for the financial year end is generally not it. Unless your business is particularly seasonal, saying *'we're really busy right now – let's delay'* is also not a good reason. It simply kicks the can down the road, exacerbating the problems that made you seek out an MRP system in the first place.

In short, understand that a manufacturing system will affect most areas of your business. Therefore, it's common sense to ensure that any department affected by such a system should be involved in its implementation. Allocating the right people, time and resources from the start, and setting the common goals from the top of the organisation will ensure that you set off on the right foot.

A plastic injection moulding company delayed implementing 123insight, citing that they were too busy due to business increasing. The MD later regretted that decision, saying; "The delay in implementation was purely down to workload and resources. In hindsight if we had implemented earlier, we would have made savings in time and effort, making our lives a lot easier." They went on to see a 200% growth in turnover without any administration staff increase, stock reduced by 10% and lead times cut from three weeks to 5-8 days.

How to implement a manufacturing system

Selecting your MRP system

Armed with your list of requirements, questions and show-stoppers, you are now ready to find, contact and grill selected vendors. How you will interact with them will differ greatly but for many expect to invest a lot of man-hours for many of your key managers.

The traditional approach will usually entail several visits to your facility from each vendor, and they'll also generally squeeze in a site visit to one of their existing customers. Maybe you'll throw in a visit to their offices just to assure yourself that they are a reputable company.

Do not underestimate how much time this will take from your business. For example, if the pre-sales process for each vendor takes, say, 2 days for 5 members of staff and you look at 5 companies, it will require 50 man-days to evaluate them!

Don't just ask about you, ask about them

In addition to knowing if they can meet your needs, you also need to understand how they do business. The obvious questions will start around cost of software but don't forget consultancy, installation and maintenance. Often, any additional reports or customisation further down the line can have a hefty invoice tag associated with them. Also, ask what the update policy is and whether software updates are included within maintenance. Software updates can have further hidden costs associated with them, as any customisation that you did with your initial version of software may have to be tweaked or even re-written completely, making updates a costly, painful and potentially dangerous process.

Remember that a Sales Accounts Manager is targeted to generate revenue, not only from the initial sale but also ongoing business every year by way of updates, customisation, training, etc.

Finally, cost plays a major part in your decision-making process. You will have an approximate price band in mind, but it's not just about the cost of the software - there's training, implementation, consultancy, ongoing maintenance and upgrade fees further down the line. How much money will you have to commit before you even start the ball rolling with training and implementation? If the system doesn't deliver, what fail-safes do you have to potentially retrieve monies already spent? You may find that you have to write a hefty cheque up-front, with no real recourse if things go pear-shaped before, during or after go-live. Make sure that you are aware of all of the hidden and ongoing charges before committing.

Subscription versus 'Buy'

Let's be clear – when you 'buy' software, you never really own it. It's purely a license to run the software. This doesn't cover support, upgrades or customisation. In recent years subscription has become more popular, with software industry goliaths such as Microsoft (Office 365) and Adobe (Creative Cloud) shifting their business models accordingly.

123 Insight was the first in the industry to offer subscription since its foundation back in 2000 – a single, low monthly cost that covers the software, support and upgrades. If you are looking at a subscription model, check to make sure that there are no hidden extras, such as version upgrade costs.

> *A company serving the rail industry reviewed 18 systems, costing up to around £39,000 with training at up to £46,000 and one system requiring 50 days of training. Some quoted annual maintenance fees of over £11,000. They did a 10-year cost analysis of 'buy versus subscription', with 123insight firmly in the 'middle of the pack', demonstrating that subscription is not necessarily more expensive over the long term.*

The 123insight difference

Here's the blatant pitch: 123 Insight's entire business model turns the evaluation process on its head and removes all the risks of the traditional approach. 123insight's USB stick and online demos consist of a dozen or so movies, broken down by job role. This allows each head of department to see how 123insight will work for them, answering many standard questions. The movies are 10-15 minutes in length and can be watched at any time, allowing staff to review them at a time that suits them, rather than having cross-department meetings, which themselves might take weeks to allow for diaries to coincide.

Next, if they like what they see they can attend a 123insight Evaluation Workshop. These 2½ hour events are held across the UK in various locations every month and are designed to answer any questions that the movies didn't cover. Attended by multiple companies, you'll often find a mix of both prospects and customers, as existing customers will send new starters in order to help them understand MRP concepts before training.

If at this stage you think 123insight will be a good fit you can attend the six days of 'No-Obligation' training, covering the complete core system. This is provided on the understanding that if, at the end of the training, you feel that the system isn't right for your business you just walk away with nothing to pay, and with a lot more knowledge than when you started. At this point you are ready to consider implementing the system yourself, you have not spent any money and have only invested six and a half days!

123 Insight Ltd does not employ any sales staff. Our mantra has always been *'If it doesn't work for you, then it doesn't work for us'*. The aim of the Demo MRP movies and Evaluation Workshop approach is to allow you to quickly decide in the minimal amount of time whether 123insight is a good fit. If it is, great! If it isn't

then you were not a genuine prospect anyway and there's nothing lost.

> *The MD of an electronics manufacturer was initially reluctant to attend an Evaluation Workshop, citing that 'the vendor should come to me, not the other way around'. After finally deciding to attend, he approached 123 Insight's MD and said; 'I got it. You are not trying to sell me anything – you are simply showing me what you have and allowing me to buy.'*

Note: Of those that decide to move forward with any MRP system within 12 months of attending an Evaluation Workshop, over 80% of them cease looking at other systems, and over 99% of companies that attend No-Obligation training go on to be 123insight customers.

Hopefully, you've now got your shortlist of vendors and you have a much clearer understanding of what you need, so it's decision time!

How to implement a manufacturing system

Decision made – now what?

At this point you have your list of requirements and a vendor that you believe can meet them. Next, you need to start thinking about what each department wants to achieve as a result of this implementation.

At the rear of this book you'll find Appendix B – a simple table that you can copy for each department head so that they can write down the objectives from their perspectives. For example, the Stores Manager may want to be able to have a quicker way to book stock in or out, thus stopping people from circumventing the system. The Sales Manager wants to be able to quickly raise quotes and convert them to sales orders as business is won. The MD or FD will be looking for better financial visibility of the order book, and so on…

We talked earlier about the importance of getting key staff on board early. Now that you have made your decision, it's even more important to keep the pace going, or even increase it. Motivation should still be high if everyone is on board with the selected system, so harness that excitement for change and get the ball rolling.

Pre-implementation tasks

You will probably already have a rough idea of some of the tasks you want to perform before implementation. Perhaps some data cleansing and/or re-shaping? Maybe you want to take the opportunity to restructure your part numbers? All of these tasks need to be noted, with key staff taking responsibility for them moving forward.

Peace-meal or all-in?

A decision needs to be made as to whether you go live across the entire company or whether you roll the system out in stages. If you are trying to extract yourself from a current painful situation then going all-in with a more competent solution will yield better results after the initial ramp-up. However, some companies prefer the 'softly-softly' approach of going live across one or two departments first and then extending the system's reach as people become more confident.

Each option has its own merits, and you'll need to make this decision based on your own circumstances. A drawback of the staged implementation is that the excitement and drive for the project can wane after the initial stage(s) when the main problems have been resolved. People then lose sight of the further benefits they can achieve with the entire project. So, if you do decide to break it down into stages, set dates for each stage and make sure that everyone understands the importance of sticking to them.

Target: The go-live date

Finally, you need to set your main go-live date. This needs to be a realistic target, otherwise motivation will wane if milestones early on are unachievable. At this stage you also need to be flexible on this. Be prepared to move it if you hit unforeseen bumps in the road. Plan the implementation to coincide with your company's quietest period during the year.

> *A fertiliser manufacturer that had outgrown its collection of Excel spreadsheets reviewed several systems costing up to £80,000, plus additional consultancy. After receiving several recommendations for 123insight they reviewed and selected it. They went live in under three months, more than halved their lead times and improved their cashflow due to forward planning of purchases.*

As mentioned earlier, a common mistake when planning a go-live date (or other milestones) is to set a date based on an event with perceived importance that actually has no real bearing. For example, some companies plan the go-live date to coincide with financial year-end – that decision, as you can probably guess, is often made by the Financial Director! In reality, as long as the relevant financial totals come across from the old to new system it does not matter whether the switch coincides with this date. Furthermore, delaying the project can have several negative impacts.

You're moving systems for a reason – delaying the go-live means that you're struggling on with the old ways and their associated problems, any memories of training will start to decay, and general enthusiasm will start to wane.

You've made the decision, so now's the time to get in gear and move forward!

Back to School – Start learning!

You have made your plan and set your target go-live date, so now you need to learn about the system you're going to implement. The method of training will differ depending on your selected system. Some vendors will require all key staff to be trained on *all* areas of the system, which will be a considerable number of man-hours away from the business and come with a hefty price tag. Although some may provide on-site training (which is often seen as a benefit), you're paying for the vendor's training staff to be on-site and it's not uncommon for systems to need 30-40 days.

Make no mistake, training is as important as the system you choose. I've often heard people disregard training, citing *'I've implemented several MRP systems before – I'll be able to do it and if I can't then there's something wrong with the system.'* That's a dangerous and, dare I say, arrogant path to take. It's like saying *'I used to repair my ten-year old Ford Fiesta when I was younger, so I'll be able to repair a brand new car with all of today's technology crammed into it.'*

Also, consider the cost of training weighed up against the cost of ignorance. One argument is often 'what if I train staff and they leave?'. The bigger risk could actually be if you don't train them and they stay! You could be opening yourself up to a wealth of problems, resentment and resistance because they don't know how to use the system, do not see the benefit of it and felt excluded from the implementation.

Things change, terminology differs, and systems have become much more comprehensive. It's important to understand the implications behind every rule and setting, and there may be more/better ways of performing tasks than those that you may have been used to previously. Again, don't repeat the mistakes of yesteryear because you have taken one system's way of doing things as the de-facto standard.

If the vendor's training allows it, you should cherry-pick which staff members get trained on specific areas of the system. For example, the Production Manager has little interest in accounts, and your accountant will not be interested in bills of materials and routings.

A watersports product manufacturer implemented 123insight in just two weeks, with the Supply Chain Manager designated as a 'Super User'. Other managers would ask his advice on how to set up certain procedures. This meant that on the occasions that he did call support, he was able to quickly communicate the requirements and understand the response due to his level of knowledge.

Identify who in each department will need *initial* training and then work out a schedule with your vendor as to when training can commence. We'll cover downstream training later. Try to combine all training to occur within as short a space of time as possible; if several weeks or months go by between the first and last person being trained a lot of information will be forgotten.

It's worthwhile for one person to be designated a 'Super User' being trained on most, if not all elements of the system. This will give them the benefit of a wider view of the system, over and above each department head. They'll see how the system will interact between departments and can help others to 'connect the dots'.

Remember that there are four stages of competence:

- **Unconscious incompetence** – the person 'does not know that they don't know'
- **Conscious incompetence** – the person is aware that they don't know or understand
- **Conscious competence** – the person knows how to perform a task but needs to concentrate when performing it
- **Unconscious competence** – the person has performed the task regularly enough that it's now second nature and can be performed easily.

The tasks you perform during training that may seem to take longer than current methods will quickly reduce as you become more adept at them.

> *The same watersports product manufacturer mentioned earlier migrated from project manufacturing to batch manufacturing. As staff got quicker performing tasks – whether they were related to using 123insight or the manufacturing process itself – the time taken dropped so dramatically that lead times were significantly improved.*

123insight requires just six days of training, with the courses broken down by job role. Prices are a low, fixed 'per-day' rate, and you can choose to only send the relevant staff to the relevant course for their role. Later, in the chapter on downstream training, we'll cover how to decide who should be sent on training and who should be trained downstream by your own staff.

Hardware first, software next

Before you can start implementing your chosen solution you'll of course need hardware to implement it on. Your business will almost certainly have an existing networking infrastructure, and this is an ideal opportunity to review it, for both now and the future.

Cloud versus local hosting

Everyone is telling you that the cloud is the place to be but what is it, what are the benefits and what are the risks?

'The cloud' is basically the name given to servers hosted on the internet. These will be managed by the online provider, so you don't have to worry about installing Operating System (OS) updates, backups, etc. You are essentially renting the hardware and OS, and in some cases the software application itself. Often, the demands of your application can be split over several servers, ensuring that if one goes down you have a level of redundancy, and the business continues as normal.

The down-side is that if your internet connection goes down, your entire business is offline. Having said that, with 4G/5G speeds surpassing that of general ADSL broadband, your business could have a 'Plan B' internet connection in place (using a Pay As You Go (PAYG) SIM card/router), which would be enough to keep the business running.

There is also the issue of security, both in terms of hacking and the stability of the vendor you choose. Ensure that you perform due diligence to confirm that the company takes security seriously and ask to see what mechanisms they have in place to mitigate against these scenarios.

Your internal PC infrastructure

Most companies will be looking to update their existing Windows-based PCs and network to support their chosen MRP system. Specifying what is required shouldn't be difficult – your vendor will no doubt have a 'System Requirements' document, detailing what you need for both client and server computers.

If you have an in-house IT department, great! They'll take all of this in their stride, quickly identifying which PCs or software will need upgrading, and they'll be able to work with your chosen vendor to handle the core software installation before implementation begins.

Many companies have just about managed to 'get by' using the existing IT skills of staff whose day job is something else. If this describes your company, then it may be more advantageous for you to outsource this task going forward. Employing an external IT company will most probably be more cost-effective and less hassle than recruiting a dedicated resource internally, and they'll have the resources to continue to stay up-to-date, both in terms of staff training and also keeping the security on your network updated.

Mobile Devices

Since the advent of tablets and smartphones many people are already carrying around in their pockets what would have been considered a supercomputer only a couple of decades back. They can connect to the company network and internet, the on-board camera can be used for functions such as scanning barcodes (perhaps to book on or off a job, or to obtain information about a works order) and they also have the benefit of requiring less user training. If your chosen system supports mobile apps or has a browser-based interface, then ensure that you factor this into the equation when looking at infrastructure.

It's worth remembering to check the minimum system requirements, especially when it comes to mobile apps. Mobile hardware can date quickly, so ensure that the app will work on your version of OS.

Remember also that if staff are using personal devices, check that data is not stored locally on them, as if the device is lost, stolen or the person moves on you could potentially lose data or have a security risk. Confirm that you can easily and immediately block a user's remote device should you need to.

Finally, ensure that your hardware infrastructure/upgrades are tested and bedded in before you move ahead with implementing a system. Otherwise, if you encounter problems you won't be able to rule out, say, a driver issue if you are seeing instability.

How to implement a manufacturing system

Data cleansing / getting ready to import

It's a guaranteed certainty that your existing data is not going to just drop smoothly into a new system, but before you look at how you're going to import it you should consider a little housekeeping.

The chance are that you won't want to transfer every piece of data. There may be customers and suppliers that you no longer deal with, along with products that have not needed to be manufactured for years. Take this opportunity to consider what data you will want to transfer and what can remain in the legacy system. Depending on your circumstances, it should still be there once your new system is up and running but will only be needed under rare circumstances.

Don't worry about the amount of data you have – that's actually not important. If you can import one record you can import a million. It's worth noting that many MRP vendors will use this as a sales technique to show their technical prowess. There will be much furrowing of brows and scratching of chins, but they'll eventually say that the import can be handled – at a price. The larger the data, the bigger the cheque.

Data import is generally performed in stages – you'll work out how to convert/reshape your data, import it into a test environment of your new system, and once you're ready to go live you'll use the same mechanisms to import the current instance of the same data into your live system.

Data types

There are two types of data that you need to take into consideration – static and dynamic:

Static data:

- Customers
- Suppliers
- Parts
- Bills of Materials
- Resources within your facility, also referred to as Work Centres
- Routings e.g. the path through the resources that items take during manufacture

Dynamic data:

- Sales Orders
- Purchase Orders
- Stock amounts (batches)

You will generally only be able to transfer your static items, but for the purpose of clarity you probably don't want or need to transfer dynamic items. You will still probably have your legacy system to refer back to, and it's often next to impossible to re-shape dynamic data between systems.

Note that you don't *have* to worry about transferring the dynamic data itself – it's only the outstanding balances that are important. For example, if you've received half of an order from a supplier, then only enter what is remaining. Ensure that you use the same order numbers as your old system for consistency.

It's important to understand that your stock and work in progress (WIP) valuation could be affected, depending on the batch costs you enter in the system. If batch traceability is important to you, then speak to your vendor to confirm the appropriate way to handle this.

Keeping continuity

Just because it's a new system it doesn't mean that you can't have continuity. Most systems will allow you to specify your starting sales or purchase order numbers, so you can continue from where your old system left off.

Part number structuring

You may already have a structure for part numbers, but this may be an opportunity to revise it or restructure it altogether. Part numbers that are just a string of letters or numbers are not easy to remember, so it's worth adding some structure to them to help make them more human-readable.

A common mistake is that companies try to cram multiple identifiers, or categories, into a part number. As a result, you end up with a part number like XXX-YY-AA-123456. This may well give you a lot of information on the part without having to look it up on a system, but this is often irrelevant and highlights a weakness in the current system's searching capabilities. A good MRP system should allow you to not only find a part through full or partial part number search, but also be capable of drilling down from batches, suppliers or any number of other routes. Everything *should* link to everything else.

Back to our part number restructuring, certainly with 123insight you would only need one level of categorisation e.g. product group. So, in the example of a PC manufacturer you might have prefixes such as:

- HDD
- CPU
- MEM
- LCD

When you are sorting your stock on-screen or working with data exported to Excel your products will automatically be grouped before applying any further filters.

Importing your data

After you've decided what to import you need to work out how to do it. No two systems are the same, so some data 're-shaping' will be necessary. We discussed earlier that some vendors will take large data transfer requirements as a buying signal and potential revenue stream, but a good system/vendor will have an easy way to get data in and good documentation to show you how to do it.

Data transfer is generally a three-stage process:

1. Export your data from your current system

2. Re-shape the data in Excel, based on your new vendor's documentation
3. Import the data into your new system

123insight offers an optional Data Import Toolkit allowing you to easily import stock details, BOMs, resources, routings, customers, suppliers, opening stock balances, open sales orders and open purchase orders from Excel spreadsheets – you are able to either set them up from scratch or populate them from your previous system.

Data import can seem like a daunting task – so many data sets, different formats, legacy and redundant data, etc. Try to focus on the opportunity of being able to cleanse, restructure and optimise your data before transferring it to your shiny new system.

How to implement a manufacturing system

Implementation – Data Transfer/Setup

W hen you start the implementation process you will invariably make some mistakes. It therefore makes sense to create your live system first, set up the basics and then replicate this into a test system. Then, once you have proven out various methodologies on the test system they can be implemented into the live structure.

The best way to help everyone to understand this is to create an implementation checklist, detailing every task for each area of the business. Each task should be grouped and prioritised so that the implementation process can be broken down into stages where each workflow can then be tested. Place an estimated time for completion against each one – once tasks are allocated to individuals it's then very easy to filter this so that everyone has clarity over their workload.

Here's a good suggestion of column headers:

- Group (e.g. Technical, Admin, Production, Stock etc.)
- Task description
- Estimated days for completion (could be whole or partial numbers)
- Critical task? (Yes/No)
- Deadline date
- Responsible person (allocated department head)
- Percentage completed

- Days left (calculated from estimated number of days minus by percentage complete)

Note: This process may or may not work for your chosen MRP system, depending on its rigidity. Some systems will allow you to use as much or as little of the software as your business needs. As a result, more inflexible systems may force you to configure additional areas of the software that you were not initially planning to use.

The implementation process (and order) can be broken down into several sub-stages:

Step 1 – Basic settings

Start by creating your employees, all settings and options. These will cover areas such as:

- Financial e.g. nominal codes, currencies/exchange rates, financial periods
- Sales and purchasing e.g. analysis codes, carriers, additional charges, supplier status settings, salutations
- Stores e.g. locations, units of measure, costs
- Administration e.g. user roles and their associated permissions

Once this is done you can create a replica test system, import your customers and test out the sales process. You may need to tweak settings in your live system, recreate your test system and try again – expect to do this a few times.

Step 2 – Companies, parts and costs

Now you're ready to import some of the data you re-shaped earlier, including:

- Companies (both sales and purchasing), addresses and contacts
- Parts and costs

You can now create a new test system and start testing the purchase ordering process.

Step 3 – BOMs, stock balances and remaining data

You've proven out the main sales and purchasing processes – now it's time to put your remaining structures in place and perform walkthroughs for each of them. Before you go live you should perform a 'pilot' – more on this later – where you'll walk through each workflow process for each department.

Mirroring changes

Do consider that once you create your live database and import data such as customers and suppliers you will then have to mirror any changes that happen in both old and new systems during this transitional period, such as companies moving or staff leaving/starting. Safeguard against such issues by making *all* staff aware of the implications of starting the data transfer process.

Keep your house in order

By now you may have replicated your live system into a test one several times over, so it's important to keep things tidy. By all means, hang on to one or two previous versions of test systems, just in case you need to refer back to a test, but once issues have been ironed out and logic proven make sure to delete the old test databases.

123 Insight provides implementing customers with a comprehensive Excel spreadsheet covering all common tasks (pictured below). Each can then be prioritised and allocated to relevant department heads, spreading the load and making it clear who is responsible for what.

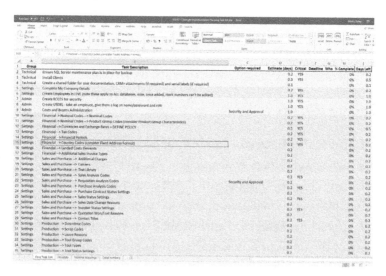

An example spreadsheet, colour-coded by category

Regular check-ins

The ball should be rolling full speed at this point, but it's important to keep an eye on the overall project, as day-to-day business can often deflect staff's attention away. Set aside some time each week for a short meeting. Pick the quietest period of your working week, which for many might be Friday pm. It doesn't have to be lengthy – 30 minutes should be more than enough. Each key member should prepare a short update on their progress, along with any questions or concerns that have been thrown up along the way.

Use your implementation tasks spreadsheet to update progress and identify tasks that are overdue. It's also worthwhile to use these events to identify anyone within the team that may be struggling and require additional assistance or training. (See next chapter for more on downstream training).

As the implementation progresses you can tick off tasks as they are completed, and you will have a clear indication of areas that require additional attention.

Hopefully, you are now feeling that you are nearing the top of the mountain and feeling confident about your choice of system and ability to successfully go live. The final stages are all about proving out real-world situations and readying the rest of the business for go-live.

How to implement a manufacturing system

Downstream training

You will already have sent your key staff on training prior to starting implementation, but as part of the implementation process you will need to decide who else needs to be sent away for training and who should receive downstream training.

Whilst the core staff that have been involved in the implementation thus far need to know the overall picture, it's probably a wise move to ensure that any remaining heads of affected departments, such as Engineering, Sales, Purchasing, Production Control, Finance and I.T., should also attend relevant vendor training.

A simple way to decide this is to complete the chart in Appendix C – Training Analysis. Write down all staff that have currently not been trained by the vendor during the initial training sessions. For each one, review how much they will need to interact with the system. Certainly, any key departmental staff or users that work across multiple departments will benefit from 'official' training rather than downstream training.

Realistically, your decision on the number of staff that you send on training may simply boil down to cost. It would be non-sensical to send your entire staff onto training, but the fact is that your implementation and go-live period will run much smoother the more staff that are competent with the system. Nobody ever complained of receiving too much training!

A company serving the food industry sent a larger than usual number of staff for training on 123insight, yet still experienced (short-term) resistance from staff that received in-house downstream training. The Commercial Director later acknowledged that more internal training should have been performed so that these staff felt included in the implementation and understood how the system affected other departments, not just their own.

Downstream training options

Every company's approach to downstream training will differ. Some companies will want as much cross-pollination of training across staff within or even across departments as possible, providing 'one to many' training. Others will limit training to only the functions and areas that each staff member will use e.g. 'one to one' training.

The problem with staff is that inevitably some will move on, taking their knowledge with them. Therefore, it's essential when performing downstream training that you create documentation to back it up.

An agricultural product manufacturer took on a graduate intern during their 123insight implementation. He was able to handle data migration and created downstream training documentation for other staff based on 123insight's supplied training manuals. As a result, the company was able to go live with minimum effort or drain on management resources. The MD noted; "He was there to ease the process, which I can highly recommend. Over that period there's a hell of a lot of crunching of figures, a lot of procedures to go through and if you don't have that right in the first stages it can be a nightmare."

123 Insight Limited help to mitigate against staff turnover through its Training Assurance programme. This allows you to take a number of training days and spread the cost into monthly payments, also saving on the cost of purchasing individual days. Training Assurance makes it easy to train new starters and removes the element of risk from your business. If the new employee leaves your company (for whatever reason) whilst still in their probationary period, we will train their direct replacement at our expense on a like-for-like basis.

Why, why oh why!

You may be aware of the '4mat' training methodology, whereby in any group there may be people that learn in one of four ways:

- **Why (and why not)?** – they need to understand the relevance of the process that they are learning.
- **What?** – they need to understand facts about a process.
- **How?** – they learn through the experience of performing a task.
- **What if?** – they learn through trial and error.

It may not be easy for you to identify who responds best to which methodology, but you will not go far wrong if you keep explaining *why* something is being done a certain way. 'Take them into their pain' – remind them of the problems they have with the previous methods and highlight the benefits of the new ones. Remember to do this not only for their specific department/job role, but so that they understand the knock-on effect within other departments.

Create training documents and Standard Operating Procedures (SOP)

This stage in the implementation process is a great opportunity to create documents that will not only help you with the downstream training process but will also assist both existing and new staff to get to grips with the system. If your vendor provides documentation in electronic format use this to cut and paste relevant content to create customised manuals for each department on standard processes. Taking this further, create simple A4 flowcharts (referred to as a Standard Operating Procedure) covering workflows both inside and outside of your MRP system. For example, a flowchart for the creation of a credit note might reference the fact that a manager must sign it off before it's raised in the system. A manual might only show the process of creating the credit note within the software, but an SOP document would reference this check and act as a quick visual guide for staff. The SOP may also relay information such as rules e.g. 'one item per line' on a sales order.

Give them the details, but with the bigger picture

Downstream training is of course all about showing people how to perform tasks relating to their specific job, but as mentioned earlier they do need to see the bigger picture.

Make sure that at the beginning of the training staff get an overview of the complete system end-to-end. Then give more focus to departments that interact with their department more regularly. For example, the sales staff need to understand the impact on lead times based on stock availability, and the Stores Manager needs to appreciate the processes that happen before and after stock is delivered/issued.

A good ratio of time to spend on this breakdown would be 10% on the company overview, 20% on the departments closest to the one being trained and the remaining 70% on their own roles.

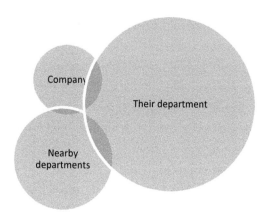

As mentioned earlier, 123 Insight provides prospective customers with a series of movies that are broken down by job role. Customers often request access to these movies (viewable online or available on a USB stick) in order to give new staff an overview of the system. All training documentation is also supplied in electronic format, allowing companies to quickly create bespoke training material.

This all works towards de-skilling the process and making the new system easy to understand. Keeping all staff that will interact with the system enthused, engaged and information will pay dividends in the end.

Y ou are now at the point where you've worked out how and what data is being transferred, you've tailored the system to your business requirements, set up routings, trained staff, etc. You're ready but not 'sure'. Before making the switch it's good practice to perform a structured 'dry run', getting staff to perform all common tasks. In 123insight terminology this is referred to as the 'Conference Room Pilot' (CRP).

Think of the CRP as an exam for your staff to see if they (and you as a business) are as ready as you can be to make the switch. Set up a computer (or more) in your conference room and set a time for staff from each department to perform their run-throughs. This would normally be set for around a week before the planned go-live date, to give you the opportunity to do any last-minute tweaks.

Fail to prepare – prepare to fail

It's critical that the person or people driving the CRP are confident in using the system *across all areas* before the event, as otherwise users will quickly lose confidence and interest if they see them struggling with it.

Ensure that all relevant data is there in order for staff to perform common tasks. Obviously, the pilot will be performed on a test database, not your live one!

Make sure that staff have enough notice period to prepare for it – the CRP is aimed to give them confidence, not to undermine it. Springing it on them will take them back to their childhood, reminding them of walking into a classroom and being told they have a test in 10 minutes! Also, ensure that they understand that this is not a training session – they should not expect to be walked through stages, but you are there to assist if they get stuck.

Create an agenda

For each department, create a list of common tasks that they would need to perform. This will differ for each business but might look something like this:

- **9:00am - Sales department**
  - Entering a new customer
  - Adding a delivery address to an existing customer
  - Email a copy of a quote to a customer
  - Raising a quote or sales order
  - Modifying price lists
- **11.00am – Purchasing**
  - Creating manual purchase orders
  - Setting up contracts
  - Chasing deliveries
  - Supplier management (vendor ratings, etc.)
- **12:30pm – Stores**
  - Booking in a purchase order
  - Release purchased items for inspection

- o   Kit a works order
- o   Performing stock-takes
- **1.30pm - Planning/Production**
  - o   Running the MRP process
  - o   Checking capacity
  - o   Reviewing and enacting MRP suggestions
- **3.00pm - Despatch**
  - o   Raising/grouping despatch notes
  - o   Pick and Pack
  - o   Adding shipping information (tracking numbers, etc.)
  - o   Adding Certificates of Conformity
- **4.00pm - Quality**
  - o   Quarantining
  - o   Managing change notes
  - o   Performance metrics
- **5.00pm – Finance**
  - o   Ability to produce sales/purchase ledgers
  - o   Raising invoices
  - o   Raising invoices in advance/post-despatch
  - o   Raising credit notes
  - o   Matching supplier invoices
  - o   Raising debit notes
  - o   Stock valuation
  - o   Work in Progress valuation
  - o   End of month accounts
  - o   Period end

Once each department has completed their tasks, sit down and review it with them. How did it go? Were there any scenarios that the system was not yet configured to handle properly? Are further tweaks required to the system before go-live?

One criticism often levied at new systems by staff at this stage is *'it takes much longer than the current way of doing things.'* Remember the four stages of learning, covered earlier? Although staff have been trained, they're still somewhere between conscious incompetence and conscious competence. They are having to think hard what to do for tasks that in a couple of weeks they'll perform with their eyes closed.

> *A company manufacturing products for the restaurant industry implemented 123insight in just 8 weeks. They stopped production on the Thursday, performed a stock check/transferred data over the weekend and went live on the Monday. The CFO commented; "We made sure that all the stock counts were right, ran some reports, and on Monday we switched it on and it worked. Production started manufacturing, accounts raised purchase orders to make sure they flowed through correctly and there were no issues. It was really a non-event, to be honest."*

Remember, although staff should see this as an exam, remind them that they are *expected* to cheat and take the answers in with them! They should feel free to refer to training material and notes – anything that elevates their confidence and provides comfort that they are moving to something better than their previous system which, for all of its problems, they undoubtedly know like the back of their hands.

How to implement a manufacturing system

Final Tasks before Go Live

The Conference Room Pilot is now complete, the feedback has been processed and any crinkles found have been ironed out. You've set a go-live date that is now only days away – what's next before you press that virtual big red button?

Typically, companies will plan the switch over a weekend or holiday period – Christmas is not uncommon, as the first week back is often slow, allowing more time to resolve any issues. Other holiday periods are also worthwhile considering if your timescale allows for it as it takes off just a little bit more pressure.

The usual process will be for staff to shut down their old systems Friday lunchtime, complete their final tasks over the weekend and start using the new system on the Monday.

These tasks will differ depending on your business but will generally include:

- **Final data transfer.** The Conference Room Pilot process will have confirmed that your data transfer methods are working, so it's now just a case of repeating this with the current live data from your old system
- **Enter outstanding sales orders.** This will generally only be any outstanding balances. So, for example, if you've ordered 10 and shipped 8 then only enter a sales order

for the remaining 2. Remember to ensure that you use the same sales order number as your old system.

- **Enter outstanding purchase orders.** Same rule applies as above.
- **Enter outstanding works orders.** Again, as above.
- **Enter stock balances.** Run a dummy period end and check the stock valuations to make sure they are close to your end position on the old system.
- **Run a final check through all settings.** Confirm that starting numbers are sequential from your old system (or in line with how you want to continue), check any other relevant settings, etc.

A mouldings manufacturer selected 123insight but delayed the implementation due to pressure of work. The MD lamented; "In hindsight if we had implemented earlier, we would have made savings in time and effort and made our lives a lot easier. The whole process of implementation was actually very easy. It was also good to have someone at 123insight Technical Support holding our hand."

At this point you should now be in a position to power down your old system, sit back and have a stiff drink, although it's important not to get complacent! The majority of the hard work is now done but you need to push especially hard to ensure that staff adhere to the new system. People will always take the path of least resistance, and there will be those that initially struggle with any new system. For now, go home, give yourself a pat on the back that you got this far and get ready with excited anticipation for Monday. (The reality is more likely to be a knot in the stomach, but if you've done the pre-work right it should be less painful than you think).

How to implement a manufacturing system

The Big Day, and beyond

I t's Monday morning, everyone is arriving into work and will be greeted by a new application that they are required to adopt. As project leader, what sort of day can you expect, and what can you do – specifically at this point – to make the transition as smooth as possible?

Handling and prioritising reported issues

The workload of most companies tends to fall into the three categories, identified by Lean Manufacturing principles as runners, repeaters and strangers:

- **Runners** - activities, problems, processes or projects you see all the time or use on a daily basis
- **Repeaters** - activities, problems, processes or projects you see regularly, but not all the time
- **Strangers** - activities, problems, processes or projects that you rarely see

The good news is that if adequate training has been provided, you'll have very few questions related to your 'runners', as staff will have been using these examples during testing. Most probably, 80%+ of your day-to-day transactions will go through smoothly and require very little intervention.

The 'repeater' category, on the other hand, is likely to generate most of your questions, as people may need a reminder of what the procedures are and how they should be handled in the new system. Although difficult to pinpoint, it may help if you can identify in advance items that might fall into this category during implementation and training this may help.

There will of course be the odd 'stranger' that pops up – perhaps a customer that ordered something once several years ago needs an urgent repeat run, so all of the relevant records (customer, BOM, etc.) need to be recreated as they weren't transferred over. Another example might be a quality fault on a batch of material. These types of event cannot be anticipated, so you just have to roll with them.

When issues arise, you should quickly categorise them, asking yourself two questions:

- Is it a must-have?
- Is it urgent?

There is an important distinction between the two and you can distil this down to four categories in which to place your issues:

- **Must-have and urgent:** Such as not being able to raise a purchase order would take priority, as it's critical to the daily operation of the business.
- **Must-have:** For example, a modification is needed to the month-end report but it's only the 7th of the month.
- **Urgent:** Items deemed urgent but not must-haves should only be dealt with once the above are resolved. Perhaps the Sales Manager wants to change the format of

printed quotes, but the current quotes are still perfectly functional for the time being
- **Not urgent:** Items such as minor customisations that don't really have a significant impact on day-to-day business

Logging issues for improvement

It's also worthwhile keeping a separate, short log of issues that arise and categorising them as to their root cause. Is it down to the defined procedure or a lack of training, for example?

Sticking with our trend of categorisation, we can break down issues to four causes:

- **Material** – e.g. the software itself. Was there a bug with the software? If yes, report it to your vendor
- **Method** – do you need to reassess the process and how the software is being used for the task in hand?
- **Man** – the good 'ol classic of 'human error', which can also be attributed to attitude during the rollout of a new system. This may require further training or another type of management intervention
- **Machine** – I.T.-related issues, covering computer or network infrastructure, which your I.T. support should address.

This allows you to view at a glance where problems are arising, so that you can quickly identify trends, affected departments or any other identifying traits that may help to gauge the effectiveness of the implementation and to plan any remedial action.

Running parallel systems – don't bother!

There's often the temptation to run the old and new systems in parallel for a set period of time. Time and again customers have said to us (despite reassurance) *'We will run the old system for a month or so, just to make sure'*. Without exception, that mantra lasts less than a week after go-live until they realise that it's simply a waste of time.

If you've done your homework up to this point and all of your tests have worked out, then there is absolutely no reason to believe it won't work with live data. Also, keeping two systems in absolute sync across all departments is nigh on impossible – the minute someone forgets to mirror data in both systems the exercise becomes pointless.

As your first week progresses you can expect issues to start tailing off as staff become more confident and competent with the system. Importantly, do not see the initial spike in questions/gripes as a failure of the implementation – it is human nature to resist change, and this is merely a reflection of the business adapting to the new system. Progressing into your second week and beyond you should see the number of issues decrease so that 95%+ of activities are performed seamlessly.

Now that the hard work of the implementation is over, and you've got over the initial learning curve you can start to turn your attentions on to how you can extend the reach of your new system within the business. What areas did you decide to consider later during the early stages of implementation? With the additional reporting the new system should be delivering you can start to analyse the data it provides to see where further savings can be made.

Your company should be firing on all four cylinders but monitoring the system's effectiveness going forward is key. Next, we'll explore some of the metrics that you should keep an eye on that will help to highlight the extent to which your new system has improved over previous methods. This may help to identify further savings going forward.

> *A company serving the rail industry implemented 123insight, going live across all departments in just four weeks. A director at the company had previous MRP implementation experience and was surprised at the ease of 123insight; "My previous experience was that implementations took a long time and required a lot of people. During the 123insight implementation process we had very little need for technical support from 123 Insight Ltd. In fact, we have only had eight support calls in the first year since going live, all of which were 'how do I do this' questions, answered in a few minutes over the phone."*

How to implement a manufacturing system

Measuring success

You've done it! A few months down the line, and the system is bedded in and working well, but how do you measure the success and, more importantly, your return on investment?

A widely acknowledged tool for categorising waste (and thereby improving performance and quality) is the Japanese philosophy of 'the seven wastes', a part of Lean Manufacturing. It is often referred to as Muda and was developed by Toyota's Chief Engineer Taiichi Ohno. These consist of:

- **Overproduction:** Making an item before it is required, which can increase lead times, storage costs and make it harder to detect defects.
- **Waiting:** Most of a product's lead time will be relating to waiting for the next operation to be performed, perhaps due to stock outages.
- **Transporting:** Having to move products between processes that are not located nearby takes time and risks damage.
- **Inappropriate Processing:** 'Using the sledgehammer to crack a nut'. For example, allocating a more costly, heavy-duty machine to manufacture something that could be done on a cheaper machine, which a better routing structure would avoid. In administration terms, doubling up on paperwork or multiple checks would be

resolved with an effective manufacturing system, as these processes would be redundant.

- **Unnecessary Inventory:** Excessive inventory makes it more difficult to spot problems on the shop floor, takes up valuable space and ties up finances.
- **Unnecessary/Excess Motion:** Related to ergonomics, such as walking, lifting, etc. With everything available on-screen rather than having to push paper around a facility the reduction in motion is greatly reduced.
- **Defects:** Quality defects must be reworked or scrapped, impacting on inventory and capacity. Defects can often be a significant percentage of total manufacturing cost, so measuring a decrease in this area gives an instantly visible indicator of the new system's effectiveness.

Every business is different, so the KPIs for a mass production business will differ greatly from one making small-run bespoke products. However, there are commonalities between all businesses, so there are certain things that you can track before and after implementation to get an idea of where savings are being made.

Stock

Invariably, this is the area that often sees the biggest and quickest benefit. When you have control over sales and purchasing trends, the amount and range of items held in stock will naturally reduce.

Stocktakes will often take much less time than before, with many companies performing cycle stocktakes instead. With the advent of mobile technologies, low-cost tablets can often now be used for booking in, out and checking stock, significantly reducing the time needed to perform tasks previously deemed labour-intensive.

> *A silk-screen printing company not only reduced their stock by 20% after implementing 123insight, but also saved £20,000 on ink. They weren't previously tracking the amount of ink being used, so ink was being made but not completely used up and then sitting on a shelf until it expired. Now, they have the required amount of ink allocated to jobs, and better stock control over any remaining ink.*

Lead times

Often a knock-on effect from having the right stock when (and where) you need it is that lead times can often tumble significantly, but that's not the only reason. Another common KPI is 'on-time deliveries' – this will undoubtedly improve when you're holding the right stock and can plan your production effectively.

When you have a better control of timings, it's often possible to identify bottlenecks or faster routes. Forward-planning ensures that extra resources can be scheduled in advance and applied when needed and quoted delivery dates become believable rather than fictional.

Purchasing Power

Once you have your suppliers and products structured within an MRP system you will have a better understanding of how you can buy more strategically. Buying in bulk for faster-moving items is a no-brainer when you have visibility of the purchasing history. Getting your purchasing under control either means increased profit margin or the ability to price your own products more aggressively.

> *A yacht canopy manufacturer implemented 123insight and reviewed all of their purchased products. When speaking with their supplier of zips they discovered that they were paying for the supplier to split their stock of 144 zips down to whatever quantity was being ordered, often resulting in errors. So, with their improved visibility of stock history they were able to strategically purchase in the supplier's stocked quantities, benefit from a price reduction and reduce errors all in one go.*

Paperwork

As we discussed right back at the start, masses of paperwork throughout a facility is often a problem that many companies are trying to solve. Many documents should now be sent electronically, such as order acknowledgements, purchase orders and invoices, often leaving only stock and production with paper, and even then, this can be reduced further.

Works orders often require additional instructional documents, which a good MRP system will allow to be associated with and viewable on-screen. Documents such as brochures could automatically be attached to a quote for a specific product. Certificates of Conformity can be attached to invoices. The list goes on. Each time you make this automatic association you remove a) the need for the paper equivalent and b) the reliance on a person to remember to attach it.

Staff time

If you pull even just some of the above examples together, you're now running a facility where staff can check and transfer stock on a mobile device, view works orders, etc. on any computer and don't spend time performing manual, repeating tasks and simply chasing their tails. When you generate large amounts of paper, you need more staff to push that paper around your business, so removing it frees up those staff for more important tasks.

123insight has produced a series of '10 Years On' case studies, available at 123insight.com, which revisit customers a decade or more after implementation. Without exception, these companies have been able to increase their turnover, often by several hundred percent, without significantly increasing the number of admin staff required to achieve this.

> *An office furniture manufacturing company implemented 123insight and halved their lead times. Consequently, as metal components were spending less time on the shop floor they were less prone to damage.*

Quality

This can be measured in several ways. Traceability is the obvious one. Audits will take a fraction of the time that they did before, as you should be able to drill down or up e.g. look at a finished part and see what it consists of and where each component came from, or look at a component and see which finished products it ended up in. Furthermore, the actual finished quality of components can be improved, simply because they are less likely to be in harm's way.

Delivery costs

With the new-found ability to forward-plan, this should give your despatch department the foresight to combine deliveries that they can see are coming down the line. Moving onto your own deliveries, the ability to take into account the true 'landed costs' of shipments of products that you receive from overseas suppliers will make your quotes more accurate.

The Human factor

The removal of stress on your employees cannot be underestimated. By simplifying the mundane you free them up for more meaningful tasks. If, perhaps you choose to implement a profit-share mechanism because of your new-found data structure, visibility and (hopefully) profit increase, then they will further embrace the system that delivers this. It can even help with personal development, as staff that may have previously been overstretched, maybe even indispensable for day-to-day business, can take time out for training. This in turn helps to safeguard your business when other staff are sick, on holiday or leave the company.

Other cost savings

There are many additional small benefits that you will notice after going live throughout your business. Some won't amount to much financially on their own, but cumulatively they quickly mount up. Stamps, paper, toner/ink, envelopes, and storage for filing are just a few examples, but maybe you can think of a few items now that you can make a note to check on once your new system is implemented.

Environmental benefits

Despite increasing exposure in the media about climate change, there seems to be little motivation by businesses to focus on the environmental impact of how they operate but implementing MRP can often positively impact on this. We've already covered the obvious ones, such as paper, toner and packaging, but it's the intangibles such as staff being able to work from home, using less power-hungry mobile devices to perform tasks.

> *A cardboard packaging company was able to provide just-in-time delivery of products to customers due to the visibility and control that 123insight provided. They were also then able to offer a waste collection service to those same customers, with the waste then used to power a bio-mass generator in their factory.*

123 Insight Ltd has been very proactive in helping its customers to measure success. At 123insight.com you can find dozens of case studies highlighting the issues companies were having that prompted them to implement MRP or replace an existing system. Each case study goes into detail about how they found the implementation process and the key areas where they were able to pinpoint quantifiable savings, along with knock-on benefits on the way.

Every business is different, but success can generally be measured by a combination of the above factors. Do take the time to think about how you want to measure success and try to identify some of those smaller knock-on benefits that can further add to the bottom line. Also, when those intangible knock-on benefits come to light, make a mental note of them so that they can be included in any future performance analysis.

How to implement a manufacturing system

Summary and Next Steps

Hopefully, you now have a clear understanding of the steps that you need to take and the obstacles that you are likely to face. Mapping out this process makes it much less intimidating, as each stage can be broken down into a series of bite-sized tasks. When you only have to look ahead towards the next step, it makes it much easier to climb the mountain.

Once you've gone through the initial steps of structuring your team and identifying your requirements, your next step is to start talking to potential vendors. Of course, I'd love you to take a look at what 123insight has to offer. We believe that we have a system that meets the vast majority of manufacturers' needs, removing the need for reliance on the vendor whilst also offering an unparalleled 'no-risk' approach with the Evaluation Workshop and 'No-Obligation' training.

I invite you to visit 123insight.com to request access to our online demo MRP movies, which you can watch anytime, anywhere and on any device.

Then, if you think 123insight might be a good fit, attend one of our Evaluation Workshops held across the UK every month. This will get all of your show-stopping questions answered in a non-sales, no-pressure environment.

If you're ready to start your implementation you can then attend the 'No-Obligation' training, and if, at the end of that, you decide that it's not suitable you walk away with nothing to pay (and with a lot more knowledge than you started with).

The 123 Insight philosophy is that we believe that manufacturers are more alike than they think, so a system should not have to be customised beyond recognition in order to meet their needs. However, if our system isn't suitable then we believe that it simply wasn't meant to be, and we wish you the best going forward.

So, now you can flick back to the beginning of this book and start making a list of your first tasks.

This book was borne from the desire to give people a path to follow, to make the best choice, implement the system in the right way and learn from the mistakes of others. I hope that it has pointed you in the right direction and that your business will benefit greatly as a result.

If you do decide to take a look at 123insight I am confident that, after reading this book, you'll have a much better understanding of what needs to be done to deliver a successful implementation. With any luck, once the system has bedded in, I'll be meeting you for a case study to highlight all the savings that the system has made to your business. Good luck!

The 123insight online demo movies

Over a dozen movies, covering areas such as sales, purchasing, engineering, production, quality and finance, allowing staff from each department to understand what a manufacturing system *should* be doing for their business.

Visit 123insight.com to register for free access.

Award-winning software

Here are just some of the awards that 123insight has either won or been finalist in. For a comprehensive list of awards please visit 123insight.com. Many of these awards are as a direct result of case studies that have been reviewed by the judging panels and have demonstrated that 123insight is a 'best in class' system provided through an unrivalled business model.

Appendix A – Project Roles

Use the following table to map out roles and responsibilities.

Name	Title	Role
		Project Director
		Project Manager
		Project Team – Finance
		Project Team – Production
		Project Team – Sales
		Project Team – Procurement
		Project Team – Engineering
		Project Team – Inventory Control
		Project Team – IT
		Project Team – Planning
		Project Team – Quality
		Project Team -
		Project Team -
		Project Team -

How to implement a manufacturing system

Appendix B – Objectives

Each member of your implementation team should write down their objectives for the implementation, in order of priority.

1. _____

2. _____

3. _____

4. _____

5. _____

6. _____

7. _____

8. _____

9. _____

10. _____

How to implement a manufacturing system

Appendix C – Training Analysis

Consider who within your company needs full training and who just requires downstream training.

Project team member	Key job functions	Direct v downstream	Course	Date	Status

How to implement a manufacturing system

Glossary of Terms

Here you will find common acronyms and words used in the manufacturing sector. Note that many are not found within this book, but you may come across them within this sector.

Advice Note	A document sent by a supplier to a customer to inform them that goods have been despatched. It usually gives details such as individual line item description, the quantity of each item and method of despatch.
Advance Invoicing	The request for an advance payment before delivery.
API	Application Programming Interface. A set of functions or procedures that allow the creation of applications which access the features/data of an operating system, application, or service.
Batch Number	A number allocated to a group of products which have common or specific properties.
BI	Business Intelligence. A technology-driven process for analysing data and presenting

actionable information (usually in a graphical format) to help staff make informed decisions.

BOM	Bill of Material. List of raw materials, components, and assemblies required to construct, manufacture, or repair a product or service.
Bonded Store	A building or other secured area in which dutiable goods may be stored, manipulated, or undergo manufacturing operations without payment of duty.
Bottleneck	Similar to pinch-point. Refers to an area within your facility where demand is greater than the resources available, resulting in a backlog at a given point within the production process.
Bill of Material	See BOM.
Capacity Planning	The process of determining your production capacity needed in order to meet customer demand.

Consignment Stock	Stock legally owned by one party but held by another.
CRM	Customer Relationship Management. Handled within 123insight using our CRM+ option, which also handles SRM and can be used for managing other internal processes.
CRP	Conference Room Pilot. A dry run through all standard processes.
E-commerce	Electronic Commerce. The process of selling products online. 123 Insight recommends Web Portal, which provides a quick and low cost way to create an online store, pushing orders into 123insight.
EDI	Electronic Data Interchange. The electronic interchange (or transfer) of business information using a standardised format. Usually used to describe the exchange of data between companies.
ERP	Enterprise resource planning (ERP) is a process by which a company manages and integrates the important parts of its business.

FIFO	First In, First Out. Used to describe the order of usage of stock items. Using FIFO, the oldest costing item will be removed first.
Finite Scheduling	The process of understanding how much work can be produced within a given time period based on the resources available for the relevant manufacturing processes.
Free Issue	Materiel provided for use/consumption at no charge to the fund subdivision that finances the activity to which it is issued.
INCOTERMS	International Commercial Terms are a series of predefined commercial terms published by the International Chamber of Commerce (ICC) that relate to international commercial law.
Infinite Scheduling	The scheduling of orders and operations without taking into account existing resource load, possibly resulting in resource overload.
JIT	Just In Time. An inventory management method where materials, goods, and labour

are scheduled to arrive or be replenished as required during the production process.

Kanban	A Japanese manufacturing system in which the supply of components is regulated through the use of an instruction card sent along the production line.
KPI	Key Performance Indicators. A measurable value that demonstrates how effectively a company is achieving key business objectives.
Lead Time	The time between the start and completion of a production process.
LIFO	Last In, First Out. Using LIFO, the most recent item added to stock will be used.
Lot Number	An identification number assigned to a specific quantity of material from one manufacturer.
Lean Manufacturing	A systematic method for the minimisation of waste within manufacturing without sacrificing productivity. This also refers to

	waste that might be caused due to fluctuations on customer demand.
Minimum Stock	The minimum level of stock that should be held for a given item.
MIS	Management Information System
MRP	Material Requirements Planning
MRP 2	Manufacturing Resource Planning
PDM	Product Data management. Often linked to PLM (Product Lifecycle Management). Related to the management and publication of product data. Also referred to as version control.
Pinch-point	An area where congestion occurs. In manufacturing this might refer to a process that is under-resourced, resulting in a backlog of work.
PLM	Product Lifecycle Management. The process of managing the entire lifecycle of a product from inception, engineering design

through to manufacturing, service and finally disposal of manufactured products.

Poka-yoke	Japanese term. A poka-yoke is any mechanism in lean manufacturing processes that helps an operator to avoid (yokeru) mistakes (poka).
Production Smoothing	Japanese term used in Lean Manufacturing: A technique for reducing the 'unevenness', which subsequently reduces waste. This is used when customer demand fluctuates.
Pro-forma	An invoice (sometimes estimated) sent by a seller to the customer in advance of shipment of goods. Often used for customs purposes. They differ from normal invoices in the fact that they are not an actual request for payment.
Quarantine	Can refer to either a store location or stock item. Used to describe an item or location for items that, perhaps for issues such as quality, should be separated from others (and generally not used).

Routing	The selection of a 'manufacturing' path through your facility.
Subcontract	The process of contracting a person/company outside of your own company to perform work as part of a larger project e.g. subcontracting of finishing work on a component.
SFDC	Shop Floor Data Collection. The process of collecting data relating to manufacturing processes. Within 123insight this would relate to the process of starting/completing a given task, which is logged through scanning of barcodes.
SDK	Software Development Kit. For 123insight, this is a product that provides a safe and secure method of passing data into 123insight from 3rd party software and systems.
SOP	Standard Operating Procedure. Refers to a document that explains the activities necessary to complete a specific task e.g. 'how to perform X'.

SRM	Supplier Relationship Management. Covered within 123insight's CRM+ product.
Serial Number	A unique identifier, containing either numbers or alphanumeric characters that is attributed to an individual item. Often abbreviated to S/N or SN.
TPM	Total Preventative /Productive Maintenance. A system for maintaining and improving the integrity of production and quality systems through its machines, processes and staff.
Visual Management	A business management technique where information is displayed using visual signals instead of text. This might take the form of different coloured clothing for different department staff, icons on signs instead of text, etc.
Vested Stock	Stock that has been set aside for a customer but with stipulations that certain conditions must be met before the stock is assigned.
WIP	Work in Progress. WIP relates to raw materials, staff labour and overhead costs

incurred for products that are at various stages of the production process.

Notes

How to implement a manufacturing system

How to implement a manufacturing system

How to implement a manufacturing system

Lightning Source UK Ltd.
Milton Keynes UK
UKHW022259141220
375052UK00009B/668